Table of Contents

2..... Good Morning to You • Come Sing with Me

3..... Smile and Show Your Dimple • Sing Some Songs with Mickey

4..... Skip to My Lou • Girls and Boys, Come Out to Play!

5..... Wake Up, Pluto • Minnie, Minnie, Oh So Pretty

6..... Where, Oh Where Has That Little Cat Gone? • Pluto Went A-Fetchin'

7..... Do His Ears Hang Low? • He'll Be Running Round the Backyard

8..... Sing Together • Rig-a-Jig-Jig

9..... P-L-U-T-O • Ring Around the Rosie

10..... On Top of the Clubhouse

11..... Found a Fishie • Oh, Dear! What Is It Mickey Sees?

12..... Did You Ever See a Froggie? • Six Little Fish

13..... Make New Friends

14..... If You're Happy and You Know It • A-Tisket, A-Tasket

15..... Beautiful Flowers

16..... Flying, Flying • Goofy, Come and Fly with Me

17..... Merrily We Fly Along • Here We Go Loop de Loop

18..... The Sky Is Blue • Under the Floating Clouds Are We

19..... The Green Grass Grew All Around

20..... This Is the Way We Cook Our Food

21..... Boom, Boom, Ain't It Great to Be Baking?

22..... Oh, How Lovely Is the Evening • Hail! Hail! The Gang's All Here

23..... Are You Hungry? • Home, Sweet Home

24..... Go Round and Round the Kitchen • One, Two, There's Lots to Do

26..... Mouseketools • For He's a Jolly Good Fellow

28..... Mickey and Pals

29..... A-Camping We Will Go • Twinkle, Twinkle, Little Star

P9-BYJ-152

Good Morning to You

Good morning to you.
Good morning to you.
Come on in the Clubhouse,
There's singing to do!

Come Sing with Me

Come sing with me, come sing with me,
It's time to turn the mic on.
Come sing with me, come sing with me,
Won't you please sing along?

Melody: Come Dance with Me

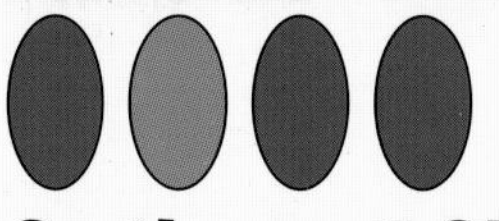

Smile and Show Your Dimple

Smile and show your dimple,
You'll find it's very simple.
You can think of something comical,
In a very little while.
Chase away the wrinkle,
Sprinkle just a twinkle,
Light your face up,
Just brace up, and smile!

Sing Some Songs with Mickey

Sing some songs with Mickey, sing them low or high.
Or sing loud or soft, but just don't be shy!
When your mouth is open, and you begin to sing,
Have a lot of fun and don't you worry 'bout a thing!

Melody: Sing a Song of Sixpence

Skip to My Lou

Skip, skip, skip to my Lou,
Skip, skip, skip to my Lou,
Skip, skip, skip to my Lou,
Skip to my Lou, my darlin'.

Girls and Boys, Come Out to Play!

Girls and boys, come out to play!
The sun is shining so bright today.
Hey there, Pluto, wake from your sleep,
And come meet your pals for a special treat!

Wake Up, Pluto

Wake up, Pluto,
Wake up, Pluto,
Wake up, Pluto,
It's time to greet the day.

Melody: Good Night, Ladies

Minnie, Minnie, Oh So Pretty

Minnie, Minnie, oh so pretty,
How does your garden grow?
With silver bells and cockle shells
And pretty maids all in a row.

Melody: Mary, Mary, Quite Contrary

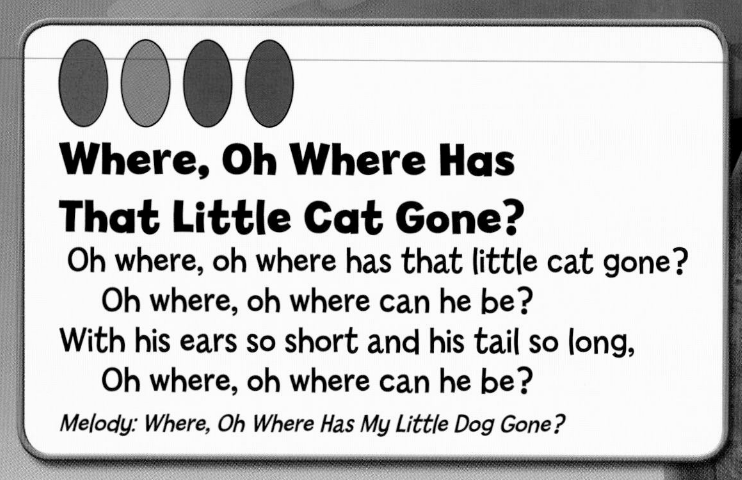

Where, Oh Where Has That Little Cat Gone?

Oh where, oh where has that little cat gone?
Oh where, oh where can he be?
With his ears so short and his tail so long,
Oh where, oh where can he be?

Melody: Where, Oh Where Has My Little Dog Gone?

Pluto Went A-Fetchin'

Oh, Pluto went a-fetchin' and he did run, uh-huh (uh-huh).
Oh, Pluto went a-fetchin' and he did run, uh-huh (uh-huh).
Oh, Pluto went a-fetchin' and he did run,
Playin' ball with Mickey is such fun!
Uh-huh, uh-huh, uh-huh.

Melody: A Froggie Went A-Courtin'

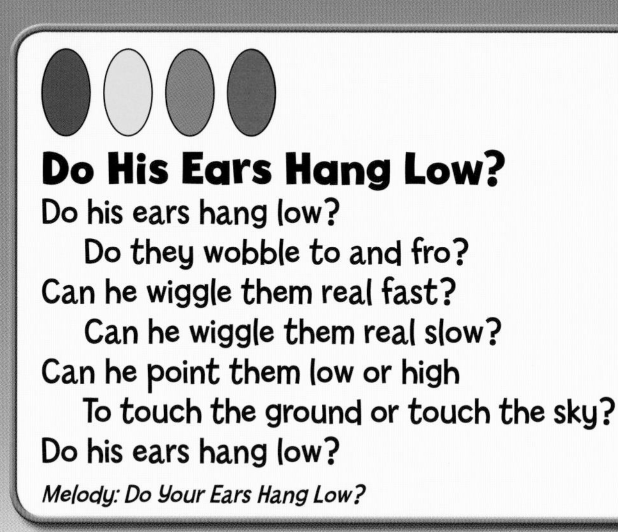

Do His Ears Hang Low?

Do his ears hang low?
Do they wobble to and fro?
Can he wiggle them real fast?
Can he wiggle them real slow?
Can he point them low or high
To touch the ground or touch the sky?
Do his ears hang low?

Melody: Do Your Ears Hang Low?

He'll Be Running Round the Backyard

He'll be running round the backyard when he runs.
He'll be running round the backyard when he runs.
He'll be running round the backyard,
He'll be running round the backyard,
He'll be running round the backyard when he runs.

Melody: She'll Be Coming Round the Mountain

Sing Together

Sing, sing together, merrily, merrily sing.
Sing, sing together, merrily, merrily sing.
Sing, sing, sing, sing!

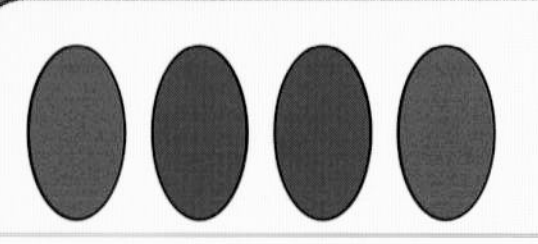

Rig-a-Jig-Jig

Rig-a-jig-jig and away we go,
Away we go, away we go,
Rig-a-jig-jig and away we go,
Hi-ho, hi-ho, hi-ho.

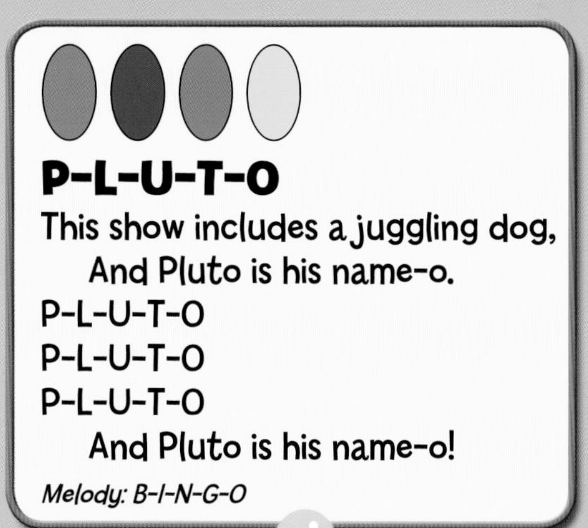

P-L-U-T-O

This show includes a juggling dog,
And Pluto is his name-o.
P-L-U-T-O
P-L-U-T-O
P-L-U-T-O
And Pluto is his name-o!

Melody: B-I-N-G-O

Ring Around the Rosie

Ring around the rosie,
A pocket full of posies,
Ashes! Ashes!
We all fall down!

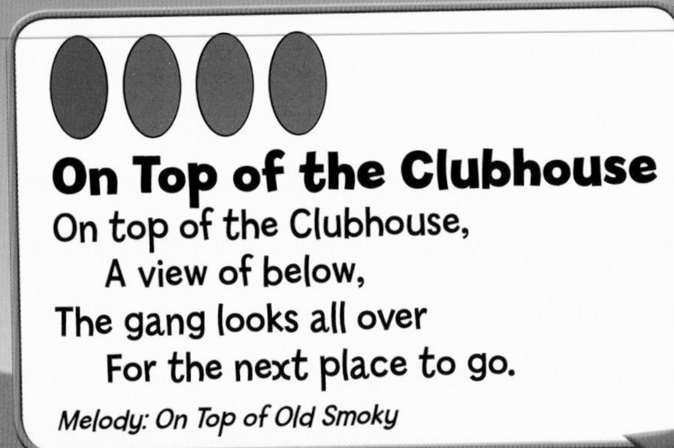

On Top of the Clubhouse

On top of the Clubhouse,
A view of below,
The gang looks all over
For the next place to go.

Melody: On Top of Old Smoky

Found a Fishie

Found a fishie, found a fishie,
Found a fishie just now.
Just now I found a fishie,
Found a fishie just now.

Melody: Found a Peanut

Oh, Dear! What Is It Mickey Sees?

Oh, dear! What is it Mickey sees?
Dear, dear, what is it Mickey sees?
Oh, dear! What is it Mickey sees?
Something that swims in the pond.

Melody: Oh, Dear! What Can the Matter Be?

Did You Ever See a Froggie?

Did you ever see a froggie,
A froggie, a froggie?
Did you ever see a froggie
As smiley as that?

Melody: Did You Ever See a Lassie?

Six Little Fish

Six little fish swim in the blue,
Big ones, little ones, red ones, too,
But the one purple fish with the great big grin,
He leads the others as they swim, swim, swim.

Melody: Six Little Ducks

Make New Friends

Make new friends, but keep the old.
One is silver, and the other gold.
A circle is round, it has no end.
That's how long that I will be your friend.

If You're Happy and You Know It

If you're happy and you know it, clap your hands.
If you're happy and you know it, clap your hands.
If you're happy and you know it,
Then your face will surely show it!
If you're happy and you know it, clap your hands.

A-Tisket, A-Tasket

A-tisket, a-tasket,
A picnic is fantastic,
Even when a silly cat
Climbs in the picnic basket!

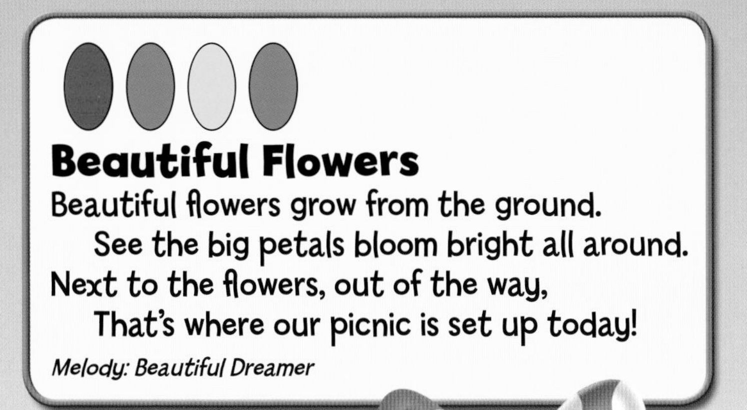

Beautiful Flowers

Beautiful flowers grow from the ground.
See the big petals bloom bright all around.
Next to the flowers, out of the way,
That's where our picnic is set up today!

Melody: Beautiful Dreamer

Flying, Flying

Flying, flying,
Into the sunny sky.
Check out the beautiful view below,
As we go soaring by!

Melody: Sailing, Sailing

Goofy, Come and Fly with Me

Goofy, come and fly with me.
We'll have lots of fun, you'll see!
Right turn first, left turn then,
Round about and home again.

Melody: Brother, Come and Dance with Me

Merrily We Fly Along

Merrily we fly along,
Fly along, fly along.
Merrily we fly along,
Over the grass and trees.

Melody: Merrily We Roll Along

Here We Go Loop de Loop

Here we go loop de loop,
Here we go loop de light,
Here we go loop de loop,
All on a Saturday night.

The Sky Is Blue

The sky is blue, dilly, dilly,
The grass is green.
The yellow sun, dilly, dilly,
Lights up the scene.

Melody: Lavender's Blue

Under the Floating Clouds Are We

Under the floating clouds are we,
Far above the land and sea.
We are so happy and carefree,
Under the floating clouds are we.

Melody: Under the Spreading Chestnut Tree

The Green Grass Grew All Around

Now in a hole (now in a hole),
There was a tree (there was a tree),
The prettiest tree (the prettiest tree),
That you ever did see (that you ever did see).
The tree in a hole, and the hole in the ground,
And the green grass grew all around, all around,
And the green grass grew all around.

This Is the Way We Cook Our Food

This is the way we cook our food,
Cook our food, cook our food.
This is the way we cook our food,
For supper time this evening.

Melody: This Is the Way We Wash Our Clothes

Boom, Boom, Ain't It Great to Be Baking?

Boom, boom, ain't it great to be baking?
Boom, boom, ain't it great to be baking?
Measuring and mixing 'til we're through,
Boom, boom, ain't it great to be baking?

Melody: Boom, Boom, Ain't It Great to Be Crazy?

Oh, How Lovely Is the Evening

Oh, how lovely is the evening,
    Is the evening.
When the stars are brightly shining,
    Brightly shining,
Shining, sparkling, twinkling.

Hail! Hail! The Gang's All Here

Hail! Hail! The gang's all here.
    Never mind the weather,
Here we are together.
    Hail! Hail! The gang's all here.
We're sure glad that you're here too.

Are You Hungry?

Are you hungry? Are you hungry?
Mousekefriends? Mousekefriends?
Dinner bell is ringing. Dinner bell is ringing.
Let's go eat! Let's go eat!

Melody: Are You Sleeping?

Home, Sweet Home

After every adventure,
Though we may roam,
We'll return to our Clubhouse,
There's no place like home.

Go Round and Round the Kitchen

Go round and round the kitchen,
Go round and round the kitchen,
Go round and round the kitchen,
And clean it up some more.

Melody: Go Round and Round the Village

One, Two, There's Lots to Do

One, two, there's lots to do.
Three, four, mop the floor.
Five, six, get the plates.
Seven, eight, stack them straight.
Nine, ten, it's tidy again!

Melody: One, Two, Buckle My Shoe

Mouseketools

Have you seen the Mouseketools,
The Mouseketools, the Mouseketools?
Have you seen the Mouseketools
That Toodles has today?

Melody: Muffin Man

For He's a Jolly Good Fellow

For he's a jolly good fellow,
For he's a jolly good fellow,
For he's a jolly good fellow,
Which nobody can deny.

Mickey and Pals

Mickey and pals, won't you come out tonight,
Come out tonight, come out tonight?
Mickey and pals, won't you come out tonight,
And camp by the light of the moon?

Melody: Buffalo Gals